ISBN 002 689298 7

MY READY-TO-READ STORIES

ILLUSTRATED BY PAMELA STOREY

STORIES BY JUNE WOODMAN

CHEX BOOKS NEW YORK

THREE DIZZY DUCKLINGS

Dilly Duck and her three
little ducklings are going
out for the day.
"We are going to the zoo,"
says Dilly.
"I like the elephants,"
says Daffy duckling.
"I like the penguins,"
says Dandy duckling.
"I like the funny monkeys,"
says Dippy duckling.

Here comes Hoppy Rabbit in his little car.

"Hop in," he says. They set off for the zoo. On the way, they meet Cuddly Cat, Merry Mole and Flippy Frog.

"We want to go too," they say. So they get into the car.

Then they meet Paddy Dog, Bossy Bear and Ozzie Owl. They all get into the car.

The car is full.
"Do not fall out," says
Dilly to her ducklings.
It is not far to the zoo.
Soon they arrive.
They all go inside.
"Keep together," says Dilly.
"Do not go too near to
the wild animals," says
Hoppy Rabbit.
They all go to look at the
lions and tigers.

The lions and tigers roar.
The ducklings are afraid.
They all run away.
"That lion is very big," says
Cuddly Cat.
"So is the tiger," says
Paddy Dog.
"Where are my three little
ducklings?" says Dilly.
"I cannot see them."

They all go to look for
the three little ducklings.
They look for them by the
giraffe house. The giraffes
are very tall. No one
can see the ducklings.
"They may have gone to see
the hippos," says Merry Mole.
So they all go to have a look.

The little ducklings are
not at the hippo house.
"The hippos are VERY big,"
says Flippy.
"But my ducklings are only
little," says Dilly.
Bossy thinks they may be
with the zebras. So they
go to have a look. But
the ducklings are not
there. Dilly begins to cry.

19

"You are silly," says Hoppy,
"Daffy likes the elephants.
We will look there."
So they go to the elephant
house. They see three big
elephants and one baby.
They see Daffy, too. Daffy
is running after the baby.
The baby is cross. It gets
Daffy with its trunk.
It swings Daffy round and
round. Then it drops Daffy.
BUMP!

Daffy begins to cry.
"I am dizzy," says Daffy.
"You are silly," says Dilly.
Flippy Frog says that Dandy
likes the penguins. So they
go to the penguin pool.
They see the penguins.
They see Dandy too. He is in
the pool. Dandy is going
round and round on
a little penguin's back.

23

"Come to me!" says Dilly.
When Dandy gets out, he falls
down. BUMP!
He is dizzy and he begins
to cry.
"Dippy likes the monkeys,"
says Bossy Bear.
So they all go to look for
the monkey house. Daffy and
Dandy walk round and round.
They are still dizzy.

They find the funny monkeys.
They find Dippy, too. He is
inside with the monkeys.
They are running after him.
Round and round they go.
Then they catch up with him.
They throw him out. BUMP!
"Come to me!" says Dilly.
But he walks round and round.
"I am dizzy," he says.
He is crying too.

"Stop it!" says Dilly. "You were all very silly."
They feel tired so they go and sit down at some little tables. They have some drinks and something to eat. They all feel better.
Then they walk round to see all the animals again.

But Dippy goes to see the elephants, not the monkeys. Daffy goes to see the penguins, not the big elephants. Dandy goes to see the monkeys, not the penguins. The lions roar, the zebras run and the giraffes look down at them. The hippos yawn.
"Home time," says Dilly.

When they get home, the
three little ducklings
jump into the pond. They
begin to swim. But they go
round and round and round.
They do look funny.
"You are still dizzy," says
Dilly Duck.
What silly
         dizzy
            ducklings!

Say these words again

zoo	round
full	drops
together	penguin
near	catch
animals	tired
lost	tables
trunk	elephant

What are they doing?

yawning

roaring

crying

swimming

running

BOSSY BEAR
at the CIRCUS

The circus is in town!
Bossy Bear loves the circus.
He runs to tell his friend,
Hoppy Rabbit.
"The circus is in town!"
says Bossy.
"I love the circus," says
Hoppy. "Come on,
we must go."
They get into Hoppy's car
and off they go.

They stop at Paddy Dog's
house. He is outside.
"The circus is in town!"
say Bossy and Hoppy.
"I love the circus," says
Paddy. "I want to go too."
"Hop into the car," says
Hoppy Rabbit.
Paddy gets into the car
and off they go.

41

They stop at the duck pond.
Dilly Duck and her three
ducklings are there with Merry
Mole and Flippy Frog.
"The circus is in town!" say
Bossy and Hoppy and Paddy.
"We love the circus. We want
to go too," say the three
little ducklings.
"Hop into the car," says
Hoppy Rabbit.
They all get into the car
and off they go.

Soon they get to the big
circus tent. They go inside.
Then the circus begins.
"Look, here come the lions!"
says Hoppy Rabbit.
The lions do lots of tricks.
"I can do tricks too," says
Bossy Bear. "Look at me!"
He runs into the circus ring.

But the lions are cross with Bossy. They hit him with their big paws and he falls down. BUMP!
"Oh! Oh! Stop it!" says Bossy. The lions roar at him and Bossy Bear runs away.
"He is very funny," say Merry Mole and Flippy Frog.
"He is very SILLY!" says Dilly Duck.

"Here come the sea lions!"
says Paddy Dog.
The sea lions are very clever.
They do lots of tricks.
"I can do tricks too," says
Bossy Bear. "Look at me!"
He goes into the circus ring
with the sea lions. He takes
a big blue ball and puts it
on his nose.

But the sea lions are cross with Bossy. They want the blue ball back. They slap him with their flippers and throw wet fish at him.

"Oh! Oh! Stop it!" says Bossy. He runs out of the ring.

The sea lions move after him.

"Bossy is funny," say Merry Mole and Flippy Frog.

"Look at the elephants!"
says Dilly to her ducklings.
The elephants go round the
circus ring. Each one holds
on to the next one's tail.
Last of all comes a little
baby elephant.
"I love the baby elephant,"
says Cuddly Cat.

Bossy runs into the ring
and pulls the tail of the
baby elephant.
"Look at me!" says Bossy
Bear.
But the baby elephant is
very cross. It slaps Bossy
with its trunk.
Bossy Bear falls down.
BUMP!
"Bossy is very funny," say
the three little ducklings.

"Look, here come the clowns!"
they all say. The clowns run
into the ring. They have
a bucket of water and a big
bucket of paste. They can do
very clever tricks. They do
not get wet. They do not
get sticky.
"I can do tricks too!"
says Bossy Bear.

"Come here, Bossy," say the clowns. "Come and be the new circus clown."
They give him a funny hat and big black boots. Then they give him a big red nose.
"Here is a funny new clown!" they all say.
"Look at me!" says Bossy Bear.

Bossy can do some tricks, but he is not so clever. His boots are much too big for him and he falls over.
BUMP!
He falls into the bucket of water. Then he falls into the bucket of paste.
Poor Bossy is very wet and very sticky.
But he does look funny!

"Stay and be a clown, Bossy,"
say the other clowns.
"Oh no, Bossy!" says Cuddly.
"Oh no, Bossy!" says Dilly.
Bossy is very wet and sticky.
He is very cross too.
"No!" says Bossy. "The circus
is no fun for a clown. I think
I will just be Bossy Bear!"

Say these words again

sticky	last
flippers	baby
paws	tail
roars	trunk
blue	bucket
throws	water
slaps	paste

What can you see?

elephant

circus tent

lion

clown

sea lion

OZZIE OWL ON THE MOON

Ozzie Owl is very clever.
He can fly high and low.
He can fly fast and slow.
"You are very clever,"
say the little ducklings.
"I wish I could fly,"
says Cuddly Cat.
"We wish we could fly," say
Bossy Bear and Paddy Dog.
"We cannot fly," say Hoppy
Rabbit, Flippy Frog and
Merry Mole.

"Yes," says Ozzie, "I am very good at flying.
I can fly high and low.
I can fly fast and slow.
But I cannot fly to the moon."
"You are silly," says Dilly Duck. "Owls do not go to the moon."
"But I want to go," says Ozzie. "I want to be the first owl on the moon."

"Owls CANNOT go to the
moon," says Dilly Duck.
"They cannot go to sleep
with all this chatter,"
says Ozzie Owl.
He flies up into his tree.
He is very cross.
"Come with me," says Hoppy.
"I know a secret place, and
I will show you."
So they all get into Hoppy's
car, and away they go.

It is a long way to Hoppy's place, but at last they get to it. It is very rocky. There are no flowers. There are no trees, and there is no grass. It is very bare. "This is my secret place," says Hoppy, "Do you like it?" "We like it," say the three little ducklings. "It is just like the moon!" say Paddy, Merry and Flippy.

"I play space games here,"
says Hoppy. "Look at my
space helmet. See how
I make my car look like
a space buggy."
Hoppy puts on his helmet.
He puts silver paper all
round his car. It looks
good.
"It looks just like a space
buggy," say Flippy Frog
and Merry Mole.

"Come back to my house,"
says Cuddly. "I have a big
box full of old things. We
can all make space suits."
Bossy has some tins of paint.
There is silver paint, too.
So they take all the paint
to Cuddly's house. Then they
get all the old things from
Cuddly's big box, and set
to work.

Cuddly has lots of old boots. She paints them silver. "They make good space boots," she says.
Bossy and Hoppy get a very big box, and make a space rocket. Flippy, Merry and Paddy Dog make space suits for everyone. Dilly makes ray guns. The three little ducklings help, but they get paint all over them.

"It all looks good," they say. They put the rocket into the space buggy. Then they put on the space suits, and pick up the ray guns.

"Time to go and get Ozzie," says Hoppy.

They all get into the space buggy, and away they go.

"This is good fun," say the three little ducklings.

They go to the forest, but
Ozzie is asleep in the tree.
"What can we do now?"
says Cuddly Cat.
"Help me," says Hoppy.
"Then we can lift him down."
Bossy and Paddy run to help.
They lift Ozzie down from
the tree. He is still asleep.
They put him in the back
of the space buggy.
He is STILL asleep.

They all get into the buggy, and Hoppy takes them back to his secret place. They run and play with all the space things.

The buggy is at the top of a little hill. Dilly Duck looks at it. It begins to go. It goes fast down the hill.

"Help!" says Dilly. "The buggy is running away!"

BUMP!
Ozzie wakes up, and looks
all round. He sees a rocky
place, with no grass and no
trees. He can see a space
rocket. He can see space men
with ray guns, too.
They run up to him.
"Help!" hoots Ozzie Owl.
"Am I on the moon?
I do not like it here!"

The buggy hits a big rock.
BUMP!
Ozzie Owl falls out of the
silver buggy. He lands with
a big bump.
"OOOOOOH!" hoots Ozzie,
"I do not like the moon.
I want to go home."
Dilly runs to help him.
"The space men will get me!"
says Ozzie.
"You ARE silly," says Dilly.

They all run up to Ozzie,
and take off their space
helmets.
"We are playing space men,"
say Bossy, Paddy and Hoppy.
"I will not go to the moon,"
says Ozzie, "but I will play
space games with you."
So they all stay and play.
They have lots of fun till
Dilly Duck says, "Home time!"

Say these words again

clever	suits
flying	space
chatter	silver
secret	paper
place	round
rocky	could
grass	asleep